Usborne Illustrated
Rhyming Stories

Usborne Illustrated
Rhyming
Stories

Retold by Russell Punter and Lesley Sims

Contents

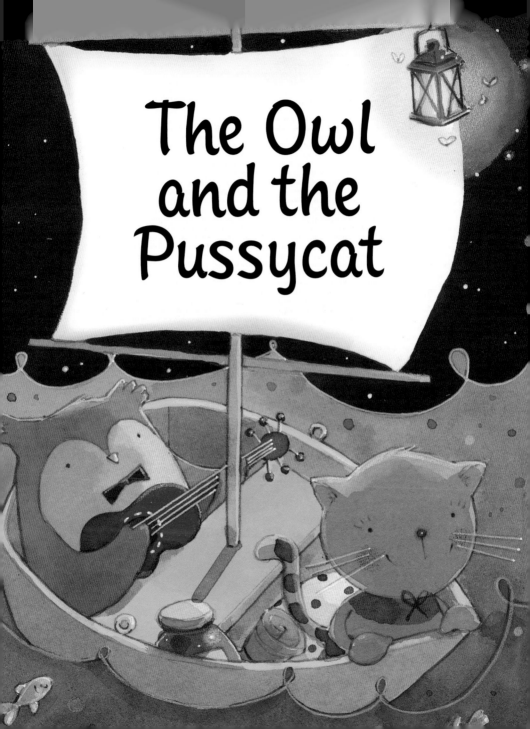

The Owl and the Pussycat

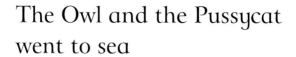

The Owl and the Pussycat
went to sea

8

in a beautiful pea-green boat.

They took some honey

and plenty of money,

wrapped up in a five-pound note.

12

The Owl looked up
to the stars above
and sang to a small guitar.

13

14

"Oh lovely Pussy!
Oh Pussy my love...

what a beautiful
Pussy you are."

18

Pussy said to the Owl,

"You elegant fowl,

how charmingly sweet you sing.

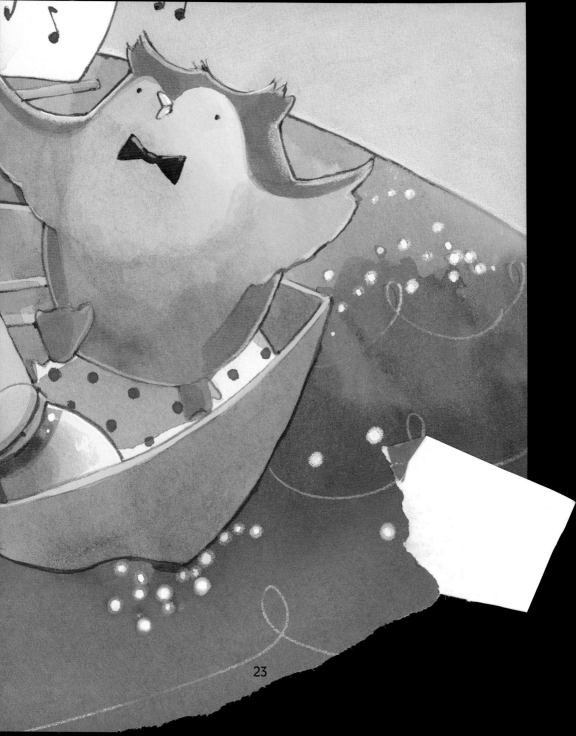

Oh let us be married –
too long we have tarried.

But what shall we do for a ring?"

They sailed away...

...for a year and a day,

to the land where the Bong-tree grows.

And there in the wood,
a Piggy-wig stood,

with a ring at the end of his nose,

his nose,

with a ring at the end of his nose.

"Dear Pig, are you willing,

to sell for one shilling,

your ring?"

Said the Piggy,
"I will!"

So they took it away,

and were married next day,

by the turkey who lives on the hill.

They dined on mince, and slices of quince,

which they ate with a runcible spoon.

And hand in hand,

on the edge of the sand,

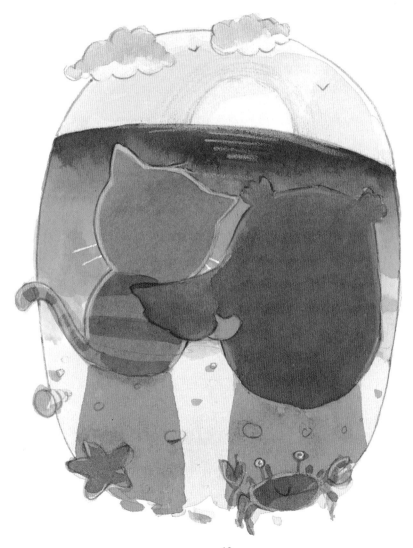

they danced by the light of the moon,

the moon,

51

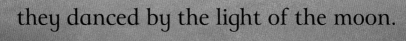

they danced by the light of the moon.

54

There was a Crooked Man

There was a crooked man...

...and he walked a crooked mile.

He found a crooked sixpence...

...upon a crooked stile.

He bought a crooked cat...

60

...which caught a crooked mouse.

And they all lived together...

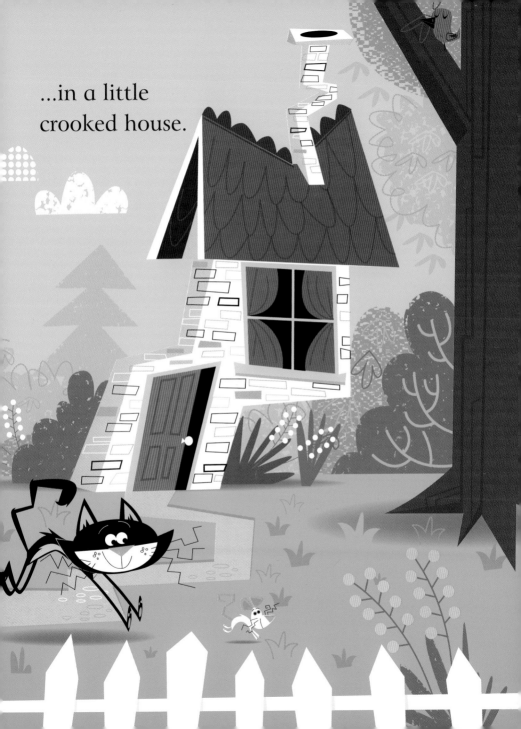

...in a little
crooked house.

The crooked man was hungry.

So he cooked a crooked fish.

His crooked cat could smell it.

And she snatched it off the dish.

The crooked man was angry.

He chased his cat outside.

He couldn't see her anywhere.

She'd found a place to hide.

The man smelled something fishy.

So he followed
where it led...

...across his crooked garden...

...into his crooked shed.

And there upon a sack...

...snuggled up against each other...

...were thirteen hungry kittens...

...and their kind but crooked mother.

80

The Old Woman Who Lived in a Shoe

There was an old
woman who lived
in a shoe.

She had so many
children...

she didn't know what to do.

There was Hannah
and Harry...

and Sara and Sam.

84

There was Aisha
and Abdul...

and Daisy and Dan.

85

There was Gwen who was greedy...

and Stan who was small.

There was Sean who was short...

and Tom who was tall.

There was Jasmine and Jeremy,
Sandeep and Grace...

boys and girls
all over the place.

Ying and Yasmin,
Jacob and Joe...

squeezed in together,
with no room to grow.

"This shoe is too full,"
said the woman, one day.

"We must get another.
I'll look right away."

With a list of the shoe stores...

Boot Boutique
34, Last Lane

Fun Feet
56, Welly Avenue

Super Shoes
22, Cobble Road

Top Shoes
1, High Heel Street

she went to them all...

But the boots were too tiny...

and the shoes were too small.

She was on her way home...

by the side of a river,

when she met
a huge giant.

He gave a sad shiver.

"Please help,"
sobbed the giant.

"There's a crab
on my toe."

96

The old woman
took hold...

and pulled it off
– just like so.

"Thanks!" said the giant.
"Now, can I help you?"

"Well," said the woman,
"I would like your shoe."

"Of course," said the giant and he gave her his shoe.

"And for being so helpful,
take the other one too."

Now all of the children
have space to have fun.

And the little old woman
can knit in the sun.

The Castle that Jack Built

106

This is the castle that Jack built.

This is the gold

that sat in the castle that Jack built.

This is the dragon who stole the gold

that sat in the castle that Jack built.

This is the wagon
that followed the dragon

WITCH 1

112

who stole the gold

that sat in the castle that Jack built.

This is the witch

who sat in the wagon

that followed the dragon
who stole the gold

that sat in the castle that Jack built.

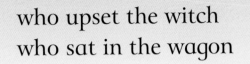

who upset the witch
who sat in the wagon

that followed the dragon

who stole the gold

that sat in the castle that Jack built.

This is the wagon turned upside down

tipped by the troll
with the scritchy itch

who upset the witch
who sat in the wagon

that followed the dragon
who stole the gold

that sat in the castle that Jack built.

This is the frog
with a grumpy frown

who hopped from the wagon
turned upside down

tipped by the troll with the scritchy itch

who upset the witch who sat in the wagon

that followed the dragon

who stole the gold

that sat in the castle
that Jack built.

This is the girl in a silver gown

who kissed the frog with a grumpy frown

who hopped from the wagon
turned upside down

tipped by the troll with the scritchy itch

who upset the witch

who sat in the wagon

135

that followed the dragon

136

who stole the gold

that sat in the castle that Jack built.

This is the prince who came to town

and kissed the girl in a silver gown.

He was the frog with a grumpy frown

who hopped from the wagon
turned upside down

tipped by the troll with the scritchy itch

who upset the witch who sat in the wagon

that followed the dragon

who stole the gold

that sat in the castle that Jack built.

This is King Jack with his golden crown.

His son is the prince who came to town

and kissed the girl
in a silver gown.

And they all lived happily
ever after,

safe in the castle that Jack built.

150

Old MacDonald Had a Farm

Old MacDonald
had a farm, E-I-E-I-O.

153

And on his farm he had some cows,
E-I-E-I-O.

When our milking
time is due, we
cows let out a great
big MOOOOOO...

154

With a moo-moo here,
and a moo-moo there...

Here a moo,

there a moo,

everywhere a moo-moo.

Old MacDonald had a farm,
E-I-E-I-O.

Old MacDonald had a farm,
E-I-E-I-O. And on his farm
he had some sheep,
E-I-E-I-O.

With a baa-baa here,
and a baa-baa there...

Here a baa,
there a baa,

everywhere a baa-baa.
Old MacDonald had
a farm, E-I-E-I-O.

Old MacDonald
had a farm, E-I-E-I-O.

162

And on his farm he had
some pigs, E-I-E-I-O.

With an
oink-oink here,

165

165

and an
oink-oink there...
Here an oink,
there an oink,

everywhere an oink-oink.
Old MacDonald had a farm, E-I-E-I-O.

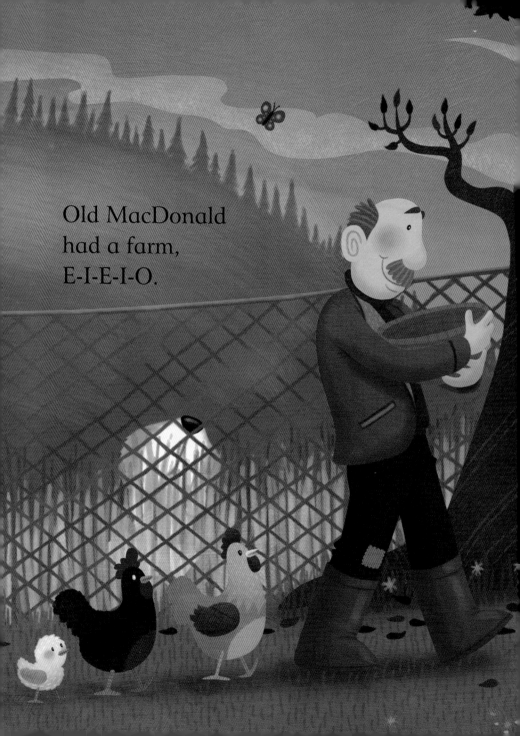

Old MacDonald
had a farm,
E-I-E-I-O.

And on his farm
he had some hens,
E-I-E-I-O.

When Old MacDonald
takes our eggs, we
fly around his head
and legs.

With a cluck-cluck here,
and a cluck-cluck there...

Here a cluck,

there a cluck,

everywhere a
cluck-cluck.

Old MacDonald had a farm,
E-I-E-I-O.

Cock-a-doodle-doo!

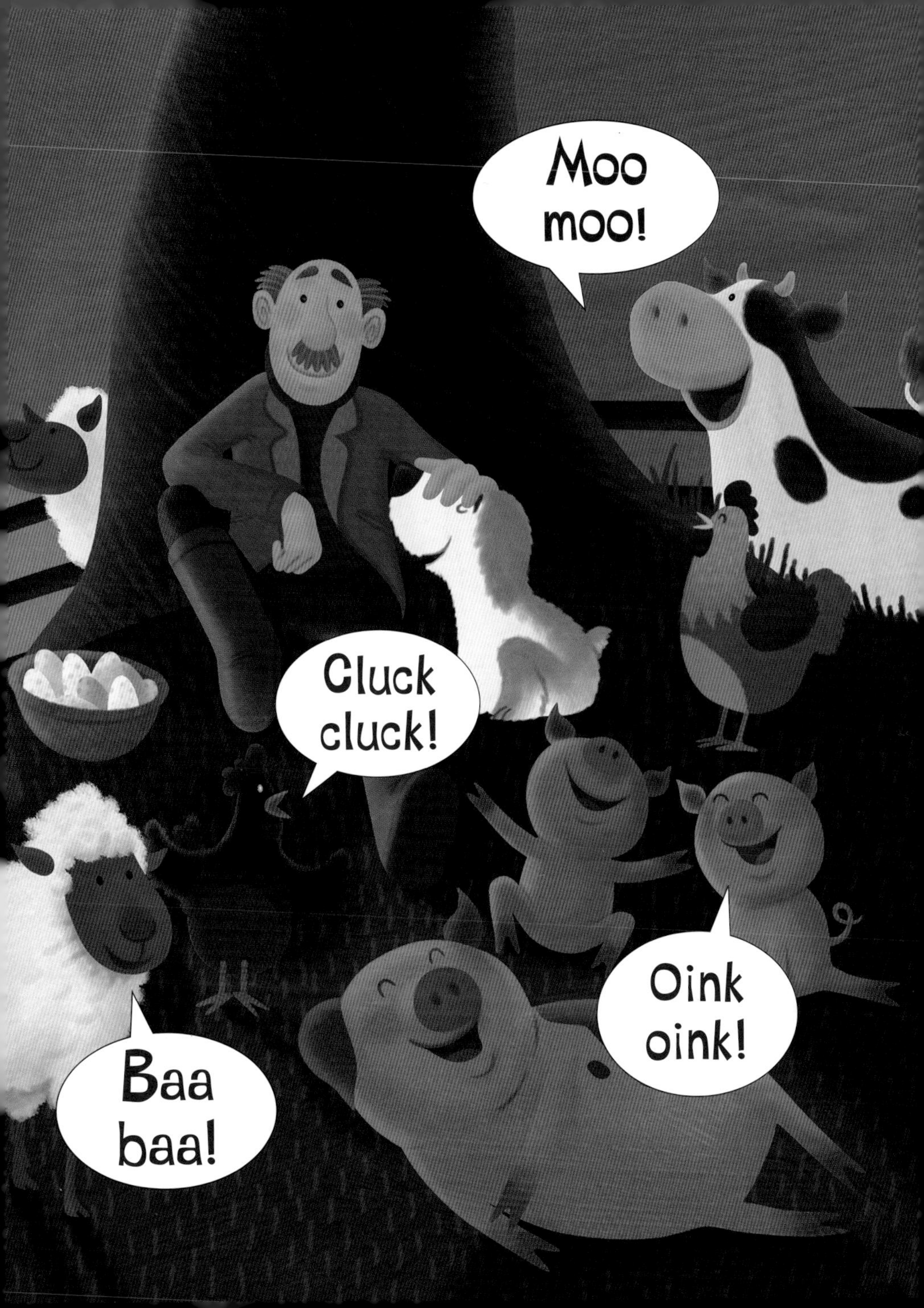
Moo moo!
Cluck cluck!
Oink oink!
Baa baa!

174

Battle of the Knights

The sign upon the castle wall
said, "Joust today open to all!"

Grand Tournament

Castle grounds
from noon
Joust today open
to all!

Sir Goldspurs read it with a grin.
"That sounds fun. I'm bound to win.
My breastplate gleams, my horse is fast.
All knights will quail as I fly past."

Sir Thomas heard him and felt glum.
He almost wished he hadn't come.

Sir Goldspurs thundered down the track – just like a rhino on attack.

An eager dog caused Tom to swerve.
It made Sir Goldspurs lose his nerve.

His lance slipped down
and hit the ground.
Inside his helmet, Goldspurs frowned.

The lance got stuck.
His horse just
stopped...

...Sir Goldspurs soared and belly-flopped.
"Oh no," he cried as he flew past.
"I didn't mean to go this fast."

He landed with a mighty splat.
(The crowd was not expecting that.)

Sir Tom raced up. "Are you alright?"
Sir Goldspurs winced. "I look a sight."

"I grazed my palm, I bashed my thumb.
My chin is feeling very numb."

"Well," said the king, "we can't avoid declaring this joust null and void."
"I disagree," Sir Goldspurs said.
He struggled up and shook his head.

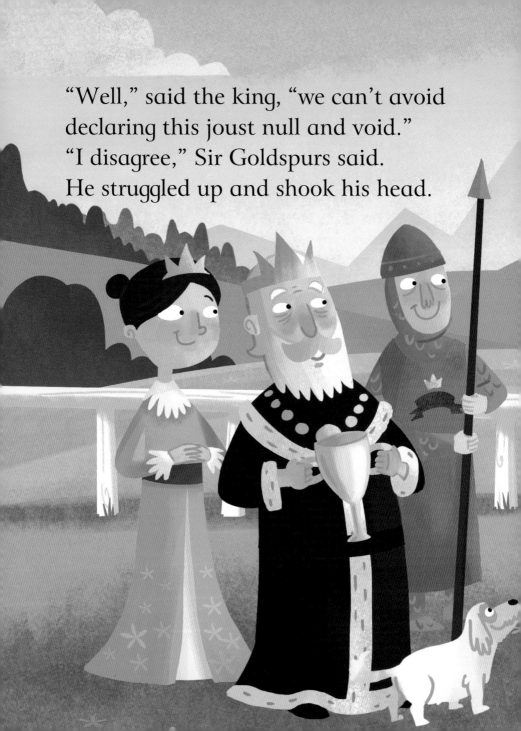

The crowd let out
a heartfelt cheer.

"Well done,
Sir Tom.
See you
next year!"

195

One, Two, Buckle My Shoe

One, two,
buckle my shoe.

Three, four,

knock at the door.

Five, six,

pick up sticks.

Seven, eight,
  lay them straight.

Nine, ten,

a big fat hen.

Eleven, twelve,

dig and delve.

Thirteen, fourteen,

maids a-courting.

Fifteen, sixteen,

maids in the kitchen.

Seventeen, eighteen,

maids a-waiting.

Nineteen, twenty,
my plate's empty.

Twenty-one, twenty-two,
"Shoo fox, shoo!"

Twenty-three, twenty-four,

home once more.

Twenty-five, twenty-six,
"Let's get this fixed."

Twenty-seven, twenty-eight,

fasten the gate.

Twenty-nine, thirty,

Gertie

"You're safe now, Gertie."

Old Mother Hubbard

Old Mother Hubbard
went to the cupboard,

to fetch her poor doggie a bone.

But when she got there,
the cupboard was bare.

And so the poor doggie had none.

Old Mother Hubbard
shut up the cupboard

and put on her warm winter clothes.

"We'll have to go out," she said with a shout,

"before all the butchers are closed."

So off down the lane, through
wind and through rain,

went Old Mother Hubbard and Spot.

'Til they came to a stop,
at Bob's Butcher's Shop.

And they went in to see what was what.

Bob the Butcher

There was plenty of meat,
for a doggie-sized treat,

but the old lady picked out a bone.

Then came the snag,
when she looked in her bag –

she had left all her money at home.

The pair stepped outside.
"Stop thief!" came Bob's cry.

And a man hurried by in a flash.

He ran with such speed,
he tripped on Spot's lead.

And went flying, along with the cash.

Bob the Butcher

"Your dog stopped that thief,"
said Bob, with relief.

"So I must reward you, my dear."

Now Old Mother Hubbard
has a very full cupboard.

And her doggie has best steak all year.

The Dinosaur Who Lost His Roar

Deep inside the forest,
Lived a dinosaur named Sid.

He used to get in trouble
For the noisy things he did.

250

He chased the birds up in the trees,

And fishes in the river.

He loved to joke,
By frightening folk.

He liked to see them shiver.

One day, he saw his old friend Spike.

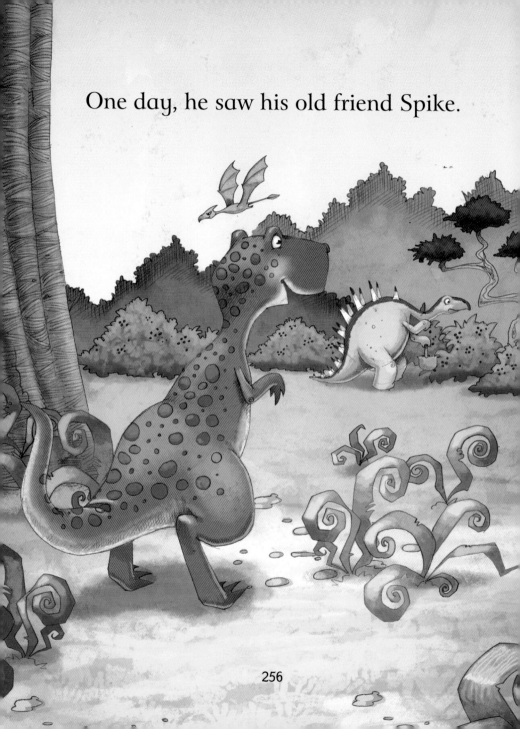

Sid crept up like a cat.

He let out such a mighty ROAR,

Spike's berries landed, splat!

"That was very funny, Spike.
You really look a fool."

Then Sid saw his good friend Ross
Bent over by a pool.

He let out such a mighty ROAR,

That Ross went tumbling, crash!

"What a brilliant dive," said Sid,
"You made a mighty splash!"

Ollybelle was hunting eggs.
Sid sneaked behind her back,

And let out such a mighty ROAR,

The eggs went flying, crack!

"An eggs-ellent surprise," laughed Sid.

"You just can't beat my roar."

But when he went to bed that night,

His throat felt really sore.

Next day he spotted Spike again
And went to play his joke.

But when he opened up to roar,
What came out was a croak.

"Sounds like your voice has gone,"
said Spike. "So goodbye mighty roar.

Any sound you care to make
Won't scare me anymore."

Sid saw Ross upon a rock,
And went to scare him off.

But when he opened up to roar,
What came out was...

...a cough.

273

"Sounds like your voice has gone,"
said Ross. "So farewell mighty roar.

Any sound you care to make,
Won't scare me anymore."

Sid was feeling bad by now,
But wanted one last try.

He tiptoed up to Ollybelle
And went to make a cry.

All he managed was a rasp,
Struggle though he might.

His tonsils felt like
two balloons,

His throat was
oh so tight.

"Your voice has gone," said Ollybelle.
"So, bye-bye mighty roar.

Any sound you care to make,
Won't scare me anymore."

Sid went home and sat alone,
Hand on throbbing head.

He took some
honey...

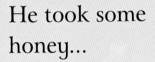
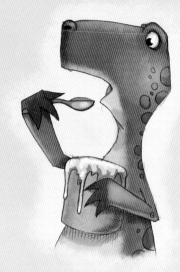

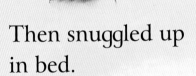

and hot,
sweet tea,

Then snuggled up
in bed.

The next day he felt better,
He skipped around his cave.

Then he started thinking
Just how he should behave.

"I must apologize," thought Sid,
"I was so very mean."

But when he reached the berry bush,
Spike was nowhere to be seen.

Ross was missing from his pool,
Sid sensed that things were wrong.

He spotted scary footprints
But to whom did they belong?

"These footprints are enormous!

They don't belong to Spike,

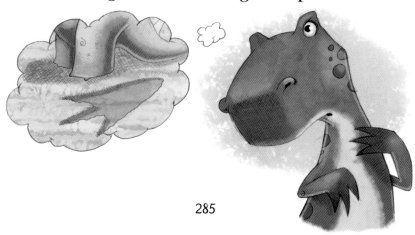

Nor Ross,

Nor little Ollybelle...

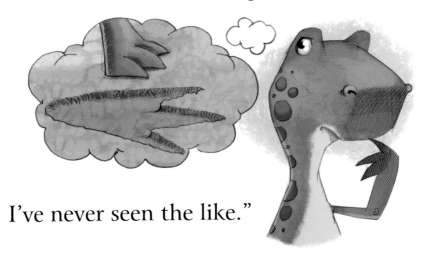

I've never seen the like."

Now poor Sid was worried.

"What will I
come to next?"

Then came a shock,
Behind a rock –
Tyrannosaurus Rex!

Sid hoped he had his voice back.
He really wasn't sure,

He took the biggest breath he could
Then let out...

...a mighty

ROAR!

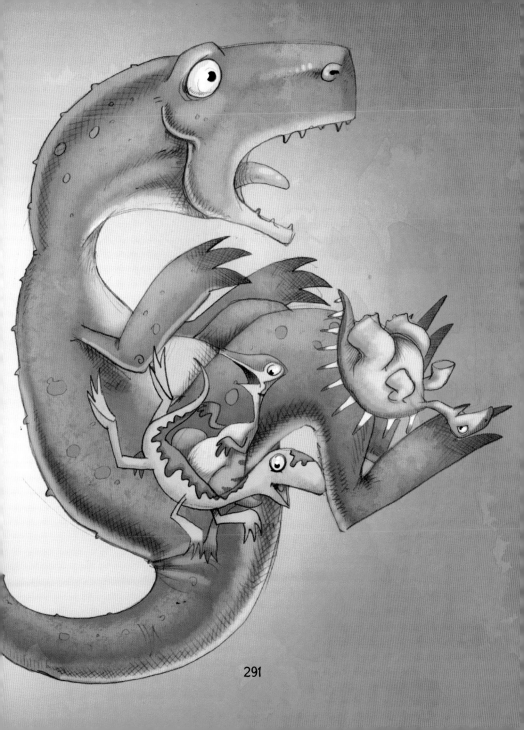

291

The T-Rex headed for the hills.
Sid's pals were safe once more,

"Three cheers for Sid the hero,

You're the greatest dinosaur!"

About the stories

The Owl and the Pussycat

was written by Edward Lear in 1867. Lear was a Victorian artist who also wrote nonsense stories and poems.

There was a Crooked Man

is based on the popular nursery rhyme.

The Old Woman Who Lived in a Shoe

is also based on a nursery rhyme. There are lots of versions from the 18th and 19th centuries – and the children are treated very harshly in some of these.

The Castle that Jack Built

is modern but was inspired by a 16th century nursery rhyme, *The House that Jack Built*.

Old MacDonald Had a Farm

is a traditional rhyme, which is often put to music.

Battle of the Knights

was written by Lesley Sims in 2010 and was inspired by a visit to Bodiam Castle in East Sussex, England.

One, Two, Buckle My Shoe

is a popular counting rhyme from the 19th century. It was written to encourage children who were learning to count.

Old Mother Hubbard

is another Victorian nursery rhyme, which has several versions. In one, the dog wears a wig and dances a jig.

The Dinosaur Who Lost His Roar

is a made-up story by Russell Punter who, like Edward Lear, loves drawing funny pictures and writing fun rhymes.

Additional designs by Caroline Spatz

First published in 2010 by Usborne Publishing Ltd., Usborne House,
83-85 Saffron Hill, London EC1N 8RT, England. www.usborne.com
Copyright © 2010 Usborne Publishing Ltd.

296